Prompt Me
Mystery & Suspense

Creative Writing Journal & Workbook

By
Robin Woods

Epic Books Publishing

Copyright © 2021 Robin Woods
First Edition

Lead Editor: Beth Braithwaite
Additional Editing: Brooke E. Wayne

Cover Design by Robin Woods

All Photos taken by Robin Woods

All illustrations taken from public domain works
via Pixabay or The British Museum

Fonts: Century, Calibri, and Destroy

Summary: A wide variety of writing prompts for maximum inspiration.

Thank you to David, Morgan, Tim, Glenn, Wendy, and Alayna for modeling for me!
You guys are awesome! xo

[Creative Writing, Diary, Non-Fiction, Reference, Writing Workbook, Fiction Writing, Writing Journal]

Paperback ISBN-10: 9781941077313

Hardback ISBN 10: 9781941077399

Table of Contents

Introduction

Writing is often messy, and sometimes we need a little help starting the process. When you begin to form your ideas, don't worry about grammar and punctuation. Simply writing the words down and experimenting are the most important parts. In order to become a better writer, you need to do three things:

1. Write often.

2. Read often.

3. Don't be afraid to make mistakes.

Embrace the mess, find your voice, and don't get discouraged.

"You can always edit a bad page. You can't edit a blank page."
— Jodi Picoult

Think of these pages as your artist's studio. Experiment with color and style. You never know; you may start something that grows into a masterpiece.

How to Use This Book

There are a variety of different styles of prompts in this workbook to help you decide what works best for you. If one style or prompt doesn't work, move on. If it doesn't work for you today, it might tomorrow.

If the pronouns don't work for you, change the she to a he, or vice versa. Prompts are meant to be inspiration, not shackles.

Carry it around with you. Mess it up. Use different kinds of ink. Stick Post-Its all over it.

Now, go forth and write!

Picture Prompts

It has often been said that a picture is worth a thousand words—but that doesn't really help writers. However, a picture can inspire thousands of words.

Use the following photos to create a unique story.

Writing Challenge:

Use at least three of the five senses in each of your stories—or add an extra sense.

☐ Sight   ☐ Taste   ☐ Touch   ☐ Smell   ☐ Hearing

There are charts in the reference section in the back.

Picture Prompt How To

We are visual beings, so let's use our graphic nature to find inspiration. Following this page, you will find fifteen photo prompts. Use each of them as a muse for a story. It can be super short or the beginnings of a novel. This is a sample of what to do. Here is my story based on this picture:

The knife slipped effortlessly between his ribs in one lethal motion. He gasped, the look of accusation in his eyes at the moment she'd betrayed him. He didn't resist as she arranged his body on the bench, missing the note clasped in his palm. He was reserving his energy while he hung onto that last bit of life.

When he heard her car disappear in the distance, he wrote a single word on the bench using his blood: "Imbroglio." It was cryptic, but he knew his partner would understand and that was all that mattered.

He drew in a deep breath. The shock had taken care of the pain and somehow had given him peace. The sun was setting, and the sky had become the most vivid red he'd seen in years. Salt air filled his nostrils, but there was no promise in it this time; his story was almost finished. But the evidence in his palm and on the bench were enough to blow this whole thing wide open.

Another vehicle pulled in behind him. From the metallic tick in the engine, he could tell it was his protégé. She was a good kid and would make a great detective someday. A few regrets flitted by as he wished he could have taught her more. Someone was calling his name now. He wondered why they sounded so, so far away.

Selene flung open the car door so hard it bounced back at her, closing on her shin. Hissing through her teeth, she pushed it open again and limped across the uneven grass to her mentor, all-the-while howling his name repeatedly. When she reached him, she dropped to her knees. There was too much blood, and the nearest medical center was an hour away. His attacker had probably known that.

"Harry," she cooed. Her voice rough and almost unrecognizable.

His eyes opened to slits, and a smile twitched for the briefest moment. A slow breath escaped his lips, then his eyes closed and he went still. When she looked at his lap, he'd opened his palm in offering. A sob caught in her throat. Her mentor was dead, but this was far from over.

1. Title: _____

2. Title: _____

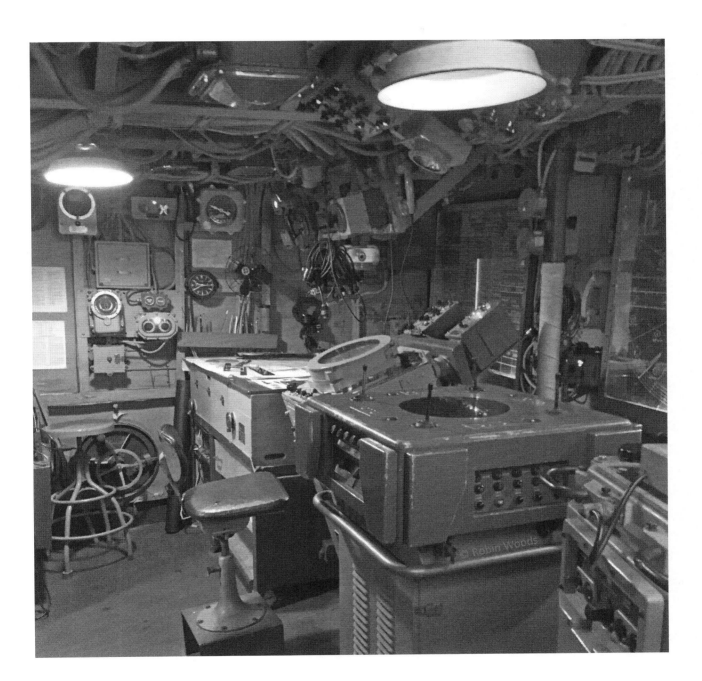

3. Title: _____

4. Title: _____

5. Title: _____

6. Title: _____

7. Title: _____

8. Title: _____

9. Title: _____

10. Title: _____

11. Title: _____

12. Title: _____

13. Title: _____

14. Title: _____

15. Title: _____

Story Starters: First Person

Emotional Standpoint: Subjective
View: Limited
Pronoun Usage: I/we/us/me/my/mine/our/ours

Writing Challenge:

Limit the amount of times your character "felt" or "feels" something. Use active voice to help keep the reader in the experience.

First Person

16. A normal person wouldn't want to kill—but I wasn't normal. Instead...

17. The detective gave me a surreptitious look for the third time. I exhaled and strolled out of the room as casually as I could manage, but...

18. Staring at the backwards name on the door, it hit me—the killer had used an anagram.

19. Scrape, plop, scrape, plop droned into the midnight hours as we shoveled the gelatinous debris off of the asphalt. The sounds started getting to me as...

20. Rumors that the house was haunted were prevalent, but I knew it was...

21. Finding a dead body in my bathroom wasn't a good start to the day; sadly, it wasn't the most shocking part...

22. Spooked, I felt for my whistle and knife in opposite pockets. Then...

23. As I closed the train door, I caught a glimpse of the mustached man in the glass. He'd been in the restaurant, across from the street vendor, and in the taxi queue...

24. The clocktower struck ten, and each gong propelled me forward with renewed...

25. I'd become the center of his attention, and I had a feeling that was the worst possible place to be...

26. The vial etched with skull and crossbones was a nice touch, I'd have to admit...

27. *Could I continue to be a bystander? Or did I need to act?* I almost danced in place with indecision, then...

28. He was my intellectual superior, but smarts weren't going to...

29. A paperclip, a pair of scissors, and a small box of matches were all I had access to at the moment; surveying the ever-shrinking room, I...

30. I had to decide whether this was theatre or murder in the next...

31. I guess I was going to have to tap into my inner Scooby and fire up the Mystery Machine—or die of curiosity. No matter what, I knew I would regret this...

32. Blaming it on ghosts was what everybody else was doing...

33. Gritting my teeth, I refused to buy into the whole conspiracy theory angle. I had the feeling that those in power were trying to discredit anyone with real information...

34. My trust in "nice" people wasn't improving in this situation. First, ...

Prompt # _____ Your Title: _____

35. Crisp air cooled the heat in my cheeks as I held the smile on my face, hoping...

36. In an instant, I was keenly focused on the waiter with the red carnation on his lapel. His hair color was different, but he was definitely...

37. The snap of the camera shutter jarred me internally. Feigning nonchalance, I turned...

38. The yellow slip of paper tumbled through his fingers before I could grab it. That second, a frigid breeze carried it into the crowd while I...

39. He told me he'd send an army after me, but I hadn't expected...

40. Well, obviously the escape room was a ruse. The clues didn't lead to an exit, but rather deeper into the...

41. I grinned at him as I tossed him the car keys. "Don't you look like an unmade bed?"

42. Each chug of the train lulled me further to sleep, but then a memory surfaced before sleep took me. The lilac perfume worn by the woman in red in the dining car...

43. There was no way in or out of this room, so I was stuck with...

44. I'd thought that tracking a serial killer would be exciting. Instead, it was piles of paper and hours of sitting in a car until...

45. It was hard to swallow past the knot in my throat. I hesitated a moment, then...

46. After an overly complicated distraction was put in motion, I moved soundlessly through the office to the file cabinet in search of...

47. I couldn't un-see the crime photos, despite doing everything I could to erase...

48. He'd jerked and shoved the file into his bag when he heard me coming. Then, he proceeded to act as if he'd been reading the paper the whole time, but...

49. *Why would Interpol show up in my blink-and-miss-it little town?* I wondered.

50. When I caught the unflinching stare of the gunman, I knew this was much more than a robbery. Stilling myself...

51. *They'd really stolen the cure for cancer.* Dumbfounded, I surveyed the room, noticing...

52. In a moment of inspiration, I grabbed a marker and played "connect-the-dots" with all the murder sites. Then, a terrifying symbol emerged...

53. I'd retired from the life, but that didn't stop them from trying to pull me back in...

54. My father was speaking the words, but I could tell he'd been coached into saying them. His word choice and cadence were off, causing me to...

Prompt # _____ Your Title: _____

55. The clockwork started to move, and I snatched my hand away before...

56. When my eyes landed on the foxglove planted beneath the window, his symptoms suddenly made sense—irregular heartbeat, small pupils, confusion...

57. Being a chemistry nerd, I knew that the products under the sink were not...

58. Homeless rarely ventured into this part of town; rumors of hauntings and a century-old mass murder kept even the brave away. Of course, I lived here...

59. A black cat screeching its way from the closet was the last thing my nerves...

60. Wishing I had James-Bond-style gadgets to help, I resigned myself to a Swiss Army knife and a book of matches to...

61. Waking at the sunrise, I found an open trapdoor in my bedroom. My stomach...

62. When I glanced at the hummingbird outside my window a second time, I realized that is was no bird at all...

63. My impulse was to be snarky, but the hollow look in her eyes made me...

64. The last victim being placed on a bench across the street from my home was not a coincidence. I was in real danger...

65. I'd allowed my own prejudice to distract me from the real truth in front of me...

66. It had remained a secret for over fifty years. Then, I came along and thought it would be romantic to publish the letters. If I'd only known that...

67. The sharp smell of mold and dust assaulted my senses when...

68. It unnerved me at the level of an Edgar Allan Poe story as I wound through the halls to find the thump, thump sound echoing in my head...

69. I had three things I was really good at: spotting flaws in logic, picking locks, and making fabulous espresso. None of those things were going to help...

70. It was the third time in two days that I'd seen the man with the navy hat...

71. I'd been branded a troublemaker by local police—but only because I kept solving cases first...

72. Just once I wanted to find a secret passage or a hollowed out book filled with jewels while in the library...

Prompt # _____ Your Title: _____

Prompt # _____ Your Title: _____

_____

_____

_____

_____

_____

_____

_____

_____

_____

_____

_____

_____

_____

_____

_____

_____

_____

_____

_____

_____

_____

_____

_____

_____

_____

Prompt # _____ Your Title: _____

Story Starters: Third Person

Third Person Limited
Emotional Standpoint: Objective
View: Limited
Pronoun Usage: he/she/it/him/his/her/they/their

Third Person Omniscient
Emotional Standpoint: Objective
View: Unlimited
Pronoun Usage: he/she/it/him/his/her/they/their

Deep Third Person
Emotional Standpoint: Subjective
View: Limited
Pronoun Usage: he/she/it/him/his/her/they/their

Writing Challenge:

Vary your language, especially your sentence openings. I.e. Not every sentence should begin with "The" or "Then."

Third Person

73. They prowled the room like detectives, though, their intent was purely sinister...

74. She opened the door to find a small parcel centered on her doormat with a single, black rose carefully placed on top. With indecision, she...

75. "Bah. It's superficial," he tisked, making light of the horrific...

76. Their loyal group spread out, each an armlength apart, and played their part in the reenactment of the crime...

77. In a shocking epiphany, she realized that this was a systemic problem that...

78. He'd managed to hide the events that had gone sideways the night before and control the narrative, but there was one weak link in...

79. Their small boat was but a toy for the hurricane force winds...

80. "Do you practice that level of cruelty, or does it just come naturally?" she asked, doing her best to keep her voice even and...

81. "Women leave far fewer clues," he shrugged with nonchalance, but...

82. He had been told to follow the money, but the money trail soon ran out. So instead, he would have to focus on...

83. She realized that the brake lines had been cut a second before...

84. Fearful he would see through her bravado, she consciously forced her body to appear apathetic and uninterested, but...

85. His son had been indicted for the crime, but had the father been the culprit...

86. Heat shimmered above the desolate road sprawling into the distance. She would have to travel at night to avoid...

87. Trying to pass for a student at university may not have been his best idea...

88. She'd taken the DNA test on a whim, not realizing the chaos that would ensue. When her phone chimed with the results, the others already knew that...

89. Fresh tattoos were etched into every inch of the day-old corpse...

90. Despite being loyal and honest to a fault, she'd been framed. Her husband thought she'd cheated, and her work believed she'd embezzled...

91. They'd deleted her life—literally. Social media, bank accounts. Everything. When she arrived home in a panic, her furniture was gone and a sour old man answered the door...

Prompt # _____ Your Title: _____

92. The clocktower bellowed into the night, covering the sounds of booted feet...

93. He removed the battery from his phone in a few simple movements, proving to her that he wasn't the simpleton he'd been playing. He was the spy she'd...

94. The screen flashed "Mom" when his phone rang, but she'd died six months ago...

95. After sliding into the driver's seat of her car, she found a half-eaten lollipop on the dashboard and sticky fingerprints all over the steering wheel and gear shift...

96. "No. You follow the money," he retorted, knowing he needed to do exactly that...

97. When he threw back the covers on his bed, he discovered that his feet were muddy and there where clumps of damp grass tracked across the wood floor...

98. An evening of scouring redacted documents was not his idea of a great first date...

99. The family gathered in the lawyer's office for the reading of the will, but one person was conspicuously absent. Before anyone could...

100. "Wait, these are real nuclear launch codes?" she squeaked before...

101. The wail of sirens leaked into his consciousness on the tide of a revelation. He couldn't trust the person who he...

102. It wasn't just the figurative use of smoke and mirrors; they'd actually used...

103. He crunched his way down the narrow passageway, barely able to stay on his feet in the blackness. When his flashlight flickered back on, he realized he was on a sea of bones...

104. The walls were covered in rusty-red writing etched into the decaying plaster...

105. When she held the map up to the light, thin dotted lines appeared beneath the maze of streets. She turned the map sideways and...

106. They'd obviously arrested the wrong person—or the killer had an accomplice...

107. Threatening letters were a way of passage for most private investigators, but when letters started to arrive at...

108. Everyone in the room was a suspect. Legitimately. He sighed as he paced...

109. He had both motive and opportunity, but it was a big leap from being angry to actually committing murder. Especially since...

110. She had selfies with celebrities and politicians on her ego wall, but none of that...

111. A string of murders had the entire city on edge. There didn't seem to be any connection between the victims in appearance, social status, or...

Prompt # _____ Your Title: _____

112. Soft snowfall carpeted the grisly scene until the victim appeared to be...

113. "Saint Killer Strikes Again" headlined the morning paper. The detective folded the paper under his arm, grumbling about...

114. Nothing seemed to be amiss, yet she couldn't shake the feeling that...

115. Being locked inside a small space was one of his greatest fears. Now he was experiencing not only that, but hearing...

116. Three people had witnessed the abduction, but not a single one was...

117. "Where's the fire?" he drawled, looking her up and down like a not-so-subtle predator. He'd been honing his game for a long time, and this was...

118. He was having an existential crisis over this case. Everything...

119. The shuffling crowd suddenly stopped in unison as if an invisible force held each of them in place. The silence...

120. She knew she was being watched, so she decided to give them a quality show...

121. "You ruined me. Not even my own mother believes in me," she paused and sighed. "You did your job well. The frame was convincing." Then, she...

122. He'd never thought of himself as a rule breaker before, but this...

123. "If you were going to off yourself, would you pay for your rent for two months in advance and fill the fridge with fresh food?" she asked her partner, who was...

124. The figure cloaked in the shadows was the key to solving the...

125. When he went to open his apartment, he noticed a new key on his ring. He froze for a moment, then looked over his shoulder down the darkened street...

126. "Can someone be one hundred percent evil?" he inquired...

127. Somehow, he'd become the villain of the story. Looking back, he knew exactly when everything had changed—it was all because of one decision that...

128. His boss had faked his death, but not for the reason everyone had assumed...

129. "Plotting multiple murders couldn't be willy-nilly. It would take patience and dedication," she sniffed. Otherwise...

130. The maze of streets presented a new challenge that had to be weighed...

131. He mused as he took a long look at the members of the conservatory and whispered to himself, "Every hero needs a villain. There are no victories without a nemesis."...

Prompt # _____ Your Title: _____

Prompt # _____ **Your Title:** _____

Prompt # _____ Your Title: _____

Use These Phrases

Writing Challenge:

Writers often forget to incorporate the sense of smell into their writings. Try to use this sense in an offbeat way. There is a chart in the back to help with inspiration.

132. **Choose and use at least six of these ten phrases:**

the bite of industrial cleaners	sneakers chirping on the linoleum
truck bumped down the road	dread spread like a virus
sluggish mind grasped	pale green light gave a sickly hue to
the sweet-sour taste of lemon drops	heat rose in waves from the asphalt
keys jingled on his sagging belt	smiled like warmth on a sunny day

133. Choose and use at least seven of these ten phrases:

laughed until she cramped	the aroma of almonds
eyes crinkling in the corners	under dusty spider webs
fluff from an angora sweater	slurped the soup down with gusto
dusted for prints	delicate hands dabbed at
stood and walked woodenly	felt gritty and unrefined

134. **Choose and use at least eight of these ten phrases:**

turned yellow-green	click of high heels drew closer
cold steel pressed against	spectacular grin wilted
papercut stung with intensity	red leather gloves
beneath the velvet sky	radio static
pen scratched the paper loudly	rationed the meager supplies

135. **Choose and use at least nine of these ten phrases:**

startling passersby	blood drained from her face
making a long cut with precision	watched the thermometer rise
smelled of bleach and insecticide	toyed with a bent paperclip
step groaned under	gasped in shock
crimson lipstick smeared	perfumed stationary

136. Choose and use at least nine of these ten phrases:

loosed the gloves from his pocket	flashlight illuminated a figure
stained antique rug	sick of disappointment
rubbed a slimy substance	heart spasmed in fright
agitated by light conversation	explosion reverberated
hot, spiced cider warming	honeysuckle and lavender wafted

137. **Choose and use at least nine of these ten phrases:**

black smoke billowed	dry, scaly skin flaked
contemptuous smile	strong scent of rosemary
surreptitious look around	clutched the book to her chest
bubbles tickling	frantically darted across traffic
air pressure in the room	chill winding its way

138. **Choose and use at least nine of these ten phrases:**

flitted about in delight	stinging wit jolted
vanilla permeated the	texture of quality satin
proved to be malleable	a malevolent phantom of late
buildings seemed to lean	grumbled his response
walked mechanically	time stretched into the distance

139. **Choose and use at least nine of these ten phrases:**

smell of damp concrete	muscles spasmed uncontrollably
curtains ruffled by the breeze	snorted with laughter
fresh lemons and basil	a split-second decision
illuminated by sunshine	watched through slits
the lightest caress	revealing a gap between his teeth

140. **Choose and use at least nine of these ten phrases:**

knees bounced in anticipation	clean air and fresh pine trees
sizzling from the kitchen	fingers sticky with honey
bland food matching her mood	warm memories washed
mustered the courage	murmur of rain enchanting
distinctive mark on his	crickets singing in the thick air

141. Choose and use at least nine of these ten phrases:

purple hydrangeas bloomed	sauntered across the street
pile of fresh whipped cream	helicopter hovered
concise use of language	could only be described as jubilant
rash course of action	wallowing in self-pity
fresh-cut grass	lavish amount of attention

choose a Path

Writing Challenge:

Use at least three of the five senses in each of your stories.

☐ Sight ☐ Sound ☐ Hearing ☐ Taste ☐ Touch

If your mystery has fantasy elements, you can always add a sixth sense.

142. **When the detective knocked at the door,...**

- ☐ a dark-eyed child swung the door open.
- ☐ scrambling and crashing boomed from inside.
- ☐ he waited to serve the search warrant.
- ☐ she knew that something terrible had happened.
- ☐ it triggered a plan of action that would impact an entire city.

143. The crime scene made...

- ☐ the headlines in papers across the country.
- ☐ passersby stop in curiosity.
- ☐ liars of them all.
- ☐ even the most hardened investigators look away.
- ☐ such an impression on a burgeoning killer, he decided to up his game.

144. **The full moon...**

☐   allowed the thief to move quickly through the maze of rooms.

☐   triggered all the crazies to cause chaos in the city.

☐   made him superstitious at this time of year.

☐   bathed the landscape in silver and shadows.

☐   gave the neighborhood watchwoman full view of the street.

145. The air seemed to thicken...

    ☐   as the walls drew closer and closer.

    ☐   the longer she was locked in the tomb.

    ☐   from a thick fog of sweat and heat.

    ☐   over the course of the unending heatwave.

    ☐   or at least it seemed to from the rising panic he felt.

146. **A shadow loomed through the glass door ...**

☐ and hesitated before finally knocking on the P.I.s office.

☐ as she hid beneath the coffee table.

☐ but it was all in his imagination—or so he thought.

☐ as it did every other day; despite this, she jumped.

☐ seconds before it splintered into thousands of pieces.

147. **Yellow police tape flapped in the wind,...**

☐ making a clacking sound next to the detectives.

☐ a forgotten shred of a covered-up murder.

☐ as the perpetrator returned to the scene to relive it.

☐ before being snatched away in the storm.

☐ the constant clack urging them to work faster.

Dialogue Prompts

A few tips before we start:

☐   Avoid using the characters' names too much in dialogue.

☐   Make sure not all of your characters sound the same.

☐   Try not to have characters parrot or repeat the previous sentence.

Writing Challenge:

Use as few adverbs as possible.

☐ Generally, people don't speak in complete sentences. Use some fragments.
☐ Play with dialect and the way your characters use contractions.
☐ Restarts, stumbles, and stutters can improve emotional scenes.

148. "Make sure it's slow acting poison."

   "You're kidding, right?"

   "What do you think I gave you?"

149. "Like Sherlock once sai—"

"Puuuhleaaase. One, he's fictional. Two, you are not a genius."

150. "I knew I'd figure it out."

"Yeah, with the help of a team of P.I.'s. I'm astounded by your magnificence."

151. "You seem to have a secret admirer."

"Lovely. I love being watched from afar…until they turn into stalkers. Then, it just becomes creepy."

_____

_____

_____

_____

_____

_____

_____

_____

_____

_____

_____

_____

_____

_____

_____

_____

_____

_____

152. "How could she have been both in the ballroom and kitchen simultaneously?"

   "Uhhh. A secret passageway, doppelgänger, mass hallucination, ghosts?"

153. "I warned you to stay away."

"Yes. But you were so blinded by your own ego that you couldn't see me for what I really am. I'm the dangerous one."

154.   "The killer left this here on purpose."

"He wants to get caught, or he wants to make you look stupid."

155. "What makes you think that you can play detective and solve this?"

"I'm the only one who believes the victim. I have to try."

More dialogue prompts...

156. "Why is there blood over here?"

    "Uhhh, I tripped and cut myself."

    "On the ceiling?"

157. "Killer clowns. Great."

    "It's like someone is enacting all of my childhood fears."

158. "It was Colonel Ketchup in the library with a meat thermometer."

    "Why do I keep you around?"

    "My good looks and sparkling conversation. Obviously. Wait, I'm rich."

159. "You know, not everyone is up to no good."

    "Nope. Just everyone we seem to run into."

160. "The last time you said 'trust me' I ended up spending the night in jail."

    "Yeah, that was funny."

    "When I murder you, no one will find the body."

161. "Don't get any of that goo on you."

    "Uhhh, hypothetically speaking, what would happen if I did?"

162. "This is the last time I'm going to trust you with the being the lookout."

    "What's my next job? Poison taster?"

Prompt # _____ Your Title: _____

Illustrated

Writing Challenge:

Try writing from a different point of view. For an added challenge, write the same scene twice, from two different perspectives.

163.   Use this illustration from the 1880s entitled "No Return" to create a story.

164. Use this classic illustration entitled "Moorish Minstrel" to create a story.

165. Use this illustration from the 1880s entitled "The Malady" to create a story.

166. Use this illustration from the 1880s entitled "Of Great Loss" to create a story.

167. Use this illustration from the 1880s entitled "Spirits" to create a story.

generate It

Writing Challenge:

Give your character a secret that influences all of his or her decisions.

Mystery Title Generator

168. Use the Mystery Title Generator to spark a story.

Mystery Title Generator

Choose your birth month and the first letter of your last name to discover your mystery title.

1. Death
2. The Hostage
3. Murder
4. The Stranger
5. Betrayal
6. The Imposter
7. Terror
8. The Girl
9. Evil
10. The Man
11. Lies
12. Smugglers

Alternate: Your mother's birth month and the first letter of your favorite food.

© *Prompt Me Series* by Robin Woods

A. in the Watchtower
B. at the Lodge
C. on Flight 13
D. in the Panic Room
E. at the Resort
F. on the Red Eye
G. in Room 101
H. at the Theatre
I. on the Waterfront
J. in the Casino
K. at the Butcher's
L. on the Ranch
M. in the Lumber Mill
N. at Midnight
O. on the Run
P. in the Sewers
Q. at the Retreat
R. on the Yacht
S. in Paris
T. at the Station
U. on the Wharf
V. in the Pavilion
W. at the Ballet
X. on the Bridge
Y. in the Hidden Room
Z. under the Bridge

169. Your new mystery character just met their arch nemesis. Set the scene.

Tragic Backstory

170. Your character has a tragic backstory that makes him/her much more relatable. Use the following to generate that story.

(Character name) _____ grew up (1)_____ in a (2) _____ (3) _____.
One day, (4) _____ (5) _____. After that, their (6) _____
(7) _____. Now, he/she (8) _____ until he/she can (9) _____.

Use the list of the right to fill in the story. Circle your choices on the right.		
He/She grew up ___	1	happily, unhappily, sheltered, poor, rich, other:
in a ___	2	bustling, sleepy, prosperous, dangerous, quiet, other:
(type of location).	3	town, city, rural village, colony, compound, fortress, other:
One day ___	4	strangers, a tornado, soldiers, a storm, a mystery man, an earthquake, the police, mercenaries, other:
(action)	5	infiltrated the area, instituted marshal law, stole (his, her, their) identities, triggered an ancient prophecy, other:
After that, their ___	6	mother, father, sister, brother, best friend, son, daughter, childhood mentor, entire family, entire community, cell-mate, co-worker, president, king, queen, regent, lieutenant, boss, other:
(what they did).	7	were kidnapped, died, were murdered, murdered someone, disappeared, disowned you, cursed you, unwittingly destroyed the livelihood of the town, insulted the head of the organized crime, gained the notice of a serial killer, other:
Now, he/she ___	8	fights injustice, is assembling a team of investigators (or mercenaries), other:
until he/she can ___	9	solve their murder, prove himself/herself, find peace, other:
Notes:		

Prompt # _____ Your Title: _____

How'd it Happen?

171. Use this generator to figure out the cause of death and spark your mystery.

CAUSE OF DEATH

The official cause of death was ____, but what really happened was that (he/she/they/you) was/were ____ by (a/an) ____.

OFFICIAL CAUSE
Last digit of your birth year

0. slipping on ice
1. railway accident
2. bee sting
3. stroke
4. falling in the shower
5. medication reaction
6. tuberculosis
7. dehydration from diarrhea
8. boating accident
9. cirrhosis (liver disease)

REAL CAUSE
Second digit of your address

0. poisoned
1. smothered
2. drugged
3. strangled
4. stabbed
5. given an air embolism
6. drowned
7. shot
8. infected
9. choked

WEAPON USED
First letter of your middle name

A. sniper
B. basket of cobras
C. ice knife
D. BBQ spit
E. old bag of cement
F. used diapers
G. rat poison
H. tarnished candlestick
I. brainwashed vigilante
J. carbon monoxide
K. syringe of doom
L. rusty razor blades
M. performing tiger
N. sharpened chop sticks
O. carrier pigeon
P. ancient amulet
Q. granola laced with glass
R. venom tipped arrow
S. butler's letter opener
T. rigged cell phone
U. sewer rats
V. battered chainsaw
W. kitchen shears
X. blow dart
Y. shephard's pie
Z. robot wasps

Alternate
Last digit of your zip code
Third digit of your phone number
Last letter of your last name

© Prompt Me Series by Robin Woods

Prompt # _____ Your Title: _____

But First, the Crime

172.   Use the W Structure ^(Who, What, Where, When, Why, & How) to plan your crime.

Who	<ul><li>Who was/were the victim(s)?</li><li>Who are the culprits?</li><li>Who are the witnesses?</li><li>Who are the suspects?</li><li>Who are the accomplices?</li><li>Who are the investigators?</li><li>Who discovered the crime(s)?</li></ul>	
What	<ul><li>What is the problem/crime/secret? (What happened?)</li><li>What was the weapon/what was stolen?</li><li>What was the motive?</li></ul>	
Where	<ul><li>Where does the overall story take place?</li><li>Where does the crime take place?</li><li>Where was the victim(s) when the crime took place? (Unless it's a murder, the victim doesn't necessarily have to be around.)</li><li>Where was the weapon(s)/stolen item or person?</li><li>Where was the culprit(s) hiding?</li><li>Where were the witnesses when the crime occurred?</li></ul>	
When	<ul><li>When did the crime take place?</li><li>When was the crime discovered?</li><li>When were the authorities called/brought to the scene?</li><li>When does the investigator find his first, second, third clues, etc.?</li><li>When does the investigator solve the crime?</li><li>When does the culprit(s) get caught/confess?</li></ul>	
Why	<ul><li>Why did the culprit commit the crime?</li><li>Why did the culprit choose that particular victim?</li><li>Why was your investigator the best one to solve the case?</li><li>Why did the crime take so long to solve? (Why did it take not long at all to solve?)</li></ul>	
How	<ul><li>How long was the overall investigation?</li><li>How did the culprit pull off their crime?</li><li>How was the culprit caught?</li><li>How did the investigator figure it out? (How did they finally piece it all together?)</li></ul>	

Prompt # _____ Your Title: _____

Roll a Story

173. Grab a die and use it to generate new challenges and fresh story ideas.

	Investigator	Victim	Suspect 1	Suspect 2
⚀	Doctor	Socialite	Domestic Partner	Banker
⚁	Private Eye	Politician	Business Partner	Lawyer
⚂	Police Detective	Reporter	Step-Child	Assistant
⚃	Secret Agent	Celebrity	Gold-Digger	Therapist
⚄	Interpol	Teacher	Social Worker	Pharmacist
⚅	Amateur Sleuth	Nurse	Exotic Dancer	Diplomat

When does the victim die?

Note: If you don't have dice, there is a paper die that can be cut out at the end of the book.

	Crime Scene	Murder Weapon	Motive
⚀	Victim's Bed	Knife	Money
⚁	Restaurant	Gun	Information
⚂	Parking Garage	Bomb	Revenge
⚃	Museum	Poison	Embarrassment
⚄	Science Lab	Rope	Betrayal
⚅	Theatre	Blunt Object	Scandal

Notes:

It's the crime, Baby

Writing Challenge:

Combine three different character archetypes into a single character for a unique blend of traits. There is a chart in the back to help.

List the Lies

Make the following list of lies conceivable. Use the lie and the plausible reason to create a story.

Why Your Character Was Late	
The Lie	The Reason
174. Hit by a snowmobile (in summer)	
175. Delayed by a pack of hyenas	
176. Birds stole the car keys	
177. Blinding solar flare	
178. The coffee was poisoned	
179. Exploding car	
180. Hit by a meteor	
181. Ravens hid his/her wallet	
182. Beavers built a dam blocking the ferry	
183. Bear trap in the bathroom	

Prompt # _____ Your Title: _____

Prompt # _____ Your Title: _____

Misfortune Bingo

Your character is confronted by a set of terrible misfortunes.

184. Pick your favorites off of the list and fill your bingo card.

1. Evicted	26. Abducted
2. Widowed	27. Fainted
3. Abandoned	28. Hexed
4. Robbed	29. Allergic reaction
5. Lost	30. Audited
6. Shipwrecked	31. Disinherited
7. Poisoned	32. Investigated
8. Fired	33. Beaten
9. Cheated	34. Slandered
10. Scandalized	35. Stranded
11. Dehydrated	36. Misdialled
12. Stabbed	37. Hard drive crash
13. Bankrupt	38. Hospitalized
14. Condemned	39. Manipulated
15. Diseased	40. Mistaken
16. Insulted	41. Tortured
17. Cursed	42. Seizure
18. Shot	43. Sneezing fits
19. Imprisoned	44. Stubbed toe
20. Humiliated	45. Pick-pocketed
21. Tripped	46. Struck by lightning
22. Shocked	47. Cell phone in the toilet
23. Bitten	48. Stepped on a rusty nail
24. Paper cut	49. Unstoppable hiccups
25. Dumped	50. Evil doppelganger

Misfortune Bingo

		Free space		

Instructions: 1. Photocopy this blank form for the number of players (or draw on paper). 2. Have each player write one favorite trope from the previous page into each box. 3. Photocopy the list of tropes and cut out each of the 65 tropes separately. 4. Draw numbers until everyone has a bingo. 5. Prizes optional.

Prompt # _____ Your Title: _____

The Misdirect

185.   Add some twists and turns with some red herrings and other fallacies.

Informal Fallacy
Herrings Are Irrelevant Distraction--Not Flawed Logic
This type of fallacy is used in everyday life. The idea/fallacy is plausible, but ultimately is a diversionary tactic because it is irrelevant to whatever is being discussed. This is not to be confused with a straw man fallacy, which purposefully distorts information. The intent to the red herring is to lead people on a rabbit trail that never had a rabbit on it.

Must-Have Literary Device
A Mystery and Suspense Staple
In writing, a red herring is a narrative element used by the writer to plant false clues and distractions to divert (and deceive) readers. Authors want to trick their audience into drawing false conclusions to set them up for a twist.

Intentional or Coincidental Red Herrings
- **An intentional red herring** is a clue that a character in the novel intentionally set up to mislead others.
- **A coincidental red herring** is a piece of information that leads people astray, but it is coincidence, not a construct of the villain (even though it is a construct of the author).

Idea List
Red Herrings are expected—here are some ways to use them:
- Give a double meaning to something--a business name, a personal letter, "last words," etc.
- A "double herring" is a clue that gets tossed aside because of new evidence, but was actually the real clue.
- Put an innocent character at the scene of the crime with a logical reason to be there.
- Incorporate red herrings into the foundation of your story, don't just toss them in.
- Have a character appear more suspicious than he/she should be.
- Leave subtle clues throughout the rising action, not just at the beginning.
- Give other characters strong motives for the crime.
- Give an object more significance than is warranted.
- Use evidence planted by the villain.
- Not all characters have to tell the truth.
- Provide conflicting clues and evidence.
- The crime should be believable.
- Introduce the detective and the villain early on.
- The crime should happen within the first quarter.
- Don't try to fool the reader, make them your partner.

Examples to Check Out
- Harry Potter--specifically the Sirius Black thread
- *The Usual Suspects*--the entire film is a red herring
- *Sherlock Holmes: The Hound of the Baskervilles*--escaped convict thread

Prompt # _____ Your Title: _____

Suspicious Suspects

186. All characters have a few things in common. Use the chart to start a story.

Suspects

All characters need three things:
1. A connection to the victim
2. A motive to kill the deceased
3. A strong feeling about the death
   This can be glee, guilt, sadness, etc.

Use this chart to create a web of suspects by filling in the info.

Victim

Name

Cause of Death

Name	**Name**	**Name**
Connection	Connection	Connection
Motive	Motive	Motive
Emotional reaction	Emotional reaction	Emotional reaction
What are they hiding?	What are they hiding?	What are they hiding?

Prompt # _____ Your Title: _____

187. Is your perpetrator a psychopath? Use the chart to start your story.

Psychopathy is a personality disorder manifested in people who use a mixture of charm, manipulation, intimidation, and occasionally violence to control others, in order to satisfy their own selfish needs.

- Glib
- Secretive
- Paranoid
- Narcissistic
- Impulsive
- Irresponsible
- Manipulative
- Authoritarian
- Lack of empathy
- Parasitic orientation
- Pathological lying
- Criminal versatility
- Superficial charm
- Seeks to blend in
- Poor behavioral controls
- Lack of realistic life goals
- Stimulation-seeking behavior
- Failure to accept responsibility
- Conventional appearance
- Grandiose sense of self-worth
- Unable to feel remorse or guilt
- Despotic need to control others
- Emotional need to justify their crimes
- Goal is complete control of their victim(s)
- Ultimate goal is to create a willing victim(s)
- Incapable of real human attachment to another
- May state readily that they want to rule the world
- Does not perceive that anything is wrong with them
- Contemptuous of those who seek to understand them
- Early childhood behavior problems & juvenile delinquency

The combination of these individual personality traits, interpersonal styles, and socially-deviant lifestyles are the framework of psychopathy and can manifest themselves differently in individual psychopaths. (Via the FBI)

Prompt # _____ Your Title: _____

Traditional prompts

Writing Challenge:

Weave in some symbolism to add depth. There is a number symbolism chart in the back.

Self-Discovery Through Hypothetical Situations

Many of these prompts are twists on well-worn topics, but creativity can spring from old favorites. These may help unlock something inside yourself, serve as interview questions, or help develop a character background.

188. You loan your phone to a stranger, then start getting strange phone calls.

189. When you get to work, everyone keeps giving you furtive glances. You ask a coworker what's going on and they answer in a riddle, confusing you further.

190. You hear breathing coming from your closed closet.

191. An envelope arrives with a series of surveillance photos of you all from over town and a note that reads, "You will be exposed for what you are." What happens?

192. You find a gym bag with enough money to buy a house. What do you do?

193. At a party, you see someone slip something into your drink. Your boss gives a toast. If you don't drink, your oversensitive boss will be insulted, risking your job.

194. You find the dead body of a complete stranger in your trunk.

195. You are forced to fake your own death, but in the process, you are able to attend your own funeral. Write the funeral service.

196. You've been murdered. Solve your own crime.

197. You wake up in the morning and realize that you've lost three days. You have ink on your fingers, a passport with new stamps, and a business card for a lawyer on your bed.

198. You have your DNA tested and find out that you are adopted.

199. At a stoplight, a stranger motions for you to pull over. The life-or-death look in his/her eyes makes comply. What happens?

200. You are making a bank deposit when robbers take over the bank.

201. You inherit a small cabin in the woods from a relative you never knew you had. When you go there, there are pictures spanning your entire life. What do you do?

202. Your new neighbor keeps showing up wearing the exact same outfit as you for weeks.

203. At the moment someone starts banging on your front door, you notice a pile of boxes marked with "POLICE DEPARTMENT" piled in the guest room. The boxes hadn't been there when you went to bed.

Prompt # _____ Your Title: _____

If You Were

If you were ___, who/what would you be? Explain by telling a story, using vivid verbs and sensory images.

204.   poison

205.   a news report

206.   a murder weapon

207.   a clue to a mystery

208.   a treasure map

209.   a magnifying glass

210.   a UV detection light

211.   an old newspaper

212.   a roadside motel

213.   a last will and testament

214.   an ATM camera

215.   a mail delivery truck

216.   a metal detector

217.   a dog collar

218.   a telescope

219.   a scalpel

Prompt # _____ Your Title: _____

Finish the Simile

Similes are comparisons using like or as that add visual appeal and help readers relate. Look at the following versions of the same actions.

A. She quietly entered the room and smiled painfully.

B. She *slipped into* the room <u>like</u> a *long-forgotten ghost,* and when she *smiled,* it was <u>like</u> *broken glass that would be the death of her.*

Now, two similes in one sentence may be a little much, but I think you get the point. They can make storytelling more powerful. Please complete the following similes, making them as powerful as possible. Then, use them in a short story.

220. He howled in contempt at me like a _____.

221. Her mind was as quiet as _____.

222. The ancient vehicle rumbled down the road like _____

_____.

223. New mysteries were unfolding like _____.

224. The slow creak of the door was like _____.

225. Wind whispered through the trees like _____.

226. The suspect looked as guilty as _____.

227. His manner was as disturbing as _____.

228. The decaying house was as uninviting as _____

_____.

229. Clues were dropping like _____.

230. Memories flooded back like _____

_____.

Prompt # _____ Your Title: _____

A Practice in Brevity

Writing Challenge:

Diversify your topics and include naanies: about a friend, a family member, and something romantic. Then tap into some emotions: happiness, sadness, indifference, and need. You could even write what would go on the tombstone of one of your characters.

A naanie is one of the most popular poems in India. It means "an expression for one and all." Writing poetry is a great way to practice precise, visual language.

Structurally, they are four lines long and have to be between 20-25 syllables. They are not bound by a particular subject or rhyme scheme. Here are a few of samples.

They can be romantic: (Totals 24 syllables)

My heart quickens when you near, 7
my skin already feeling your touch. 9
Joy enraptures me. 5
You are home. 3

—Robin Woods

Or even sinister: (Totals 24 syllables)

I smile. 3
Hiding my malevolence. 7
Your duplicitous nature will be revealed— 12
By me. 2

—Robin Woods

Or even inspirational: (Totals 22 syllables)

What we need is— 4
Kindness. 2
For everyone to let go of me—and think of we. 13
Be the change. 3

—Robin Woods

231.   About love:

_____

_____

_____

_____

232.   About loss:

_____

_____

_____

_____

233.   About joy:

_____

_____

_____

_____

234.   About friendship:

_____

_____

_____

_____

235.   About the city:

_____

_____

_____

_____

236.   From the perspective of a murderer:

_____

_____

_____

_____

237.   From the perspective of a murder victim:

_____

_____

_____

_____

238.   Your choice:

_____

_____

_____

_____

journal

Writing Challenge:

Use this space as a traditional journal, or for a list of story ideas that were inspired by the prompts.

Reference

References within the Workbook

My Notes & Lists:

Serial Murder According to the FBI

Serial Murder According to the FBI

General Notes

- A serial murderer may have multiple motives for committing his crimes.
- Motives may evolve both within a single murder, as well throughout the murder series.
- Regardless of the motive, serial murderers commit their crimes because they want to. The exception to this would be those few killers suffering from a severe mental illness.

Motives to Kill

- **Anger:** The offender displays rage or hostility towards a certain subgroup of the population or with society as a whole.
- **Power or Thrill:** The motivation in which the offender feels empowered and/or excited when he kills his victims.
- **Criminal Enterprise:** The offender benefits in status or monetary compensation by committing murder that is drug, gang, or organized crime related.
- **Financial Gain:** The offender benefits monetarily from killing. Examples of these types of crimes are "black widow" killings, robbery homicides, or multiple killings involving insurance or welfare fraud.
- **Ideology:** A motivation to commit murders in order to further the goals and ideas of a specific individual or group. Eg. terrorist groups or an individual(s) who attacks a specific racial, gender, or ethnic group.
- **Psychosis:** A situation in which the offender is suffering from a severe mental illness and is killing because of that illness. This may include auditory and/or visual hallucinations and paranoid, grandiose, or bizarre delusions.
- **Sexually-based:** A motivation driven by the sexual needs/desires of the offender. There may or may not be overt sexual contact reflected in the crime scene.

Victim Selection

An offender selects a victim, regardless of the category, based upon availability, vulnerability, and desirability.

- **Availability:** The victim's lifestyle or circumstances that allow the offender access to the victim.
- **Vulnerability:** The degree to which the victim is susceptible to attack by the offender.
- **Desirability:** The appeal of the victim to the offender that may include race, gender, ethnic background, age of the victim, or other specific preferences the offender determines.

Serial Killer Myths

- Serial killers are all dysfunctional loners.
- Serial killers are all white males.
- Serial killers are only motivated by sex.
- Serial killers want to get caught.
- Serial killers cannot stop killing.
- Serial killers are insane or are evil geniuses.
- Serial killers travel and operate interstate.

The Federal Bureau of Investigation (FBI) hosted a multi-disciplinary symposium in 2005. The goal of the Symposium was to bring together a group of respected experts on serial murder from a variety of fields and specialties, to identify the commonalities of knowledge regarding serial murder. These are excerpts and notes based on a published article online at https://www.fbi.gov/stats-services/publications/serial-murder#seven

Character Motivations

In order to have a well-rounded character, they should have multiple reasons that motivate them to do the things they do. No character is purely good or evil, but a mixture of both.

Reasons for Characters to Act			
Acceptance	Disgust	Justice	Rage
Adventure	Duty	Knowledge	Rebellion
Alienation	Eagerness	Legacy	Reconciliation
Ambition	Empathy	Loneliness	Redemption
Anxiety	Envy	Loss	Regret
Avoidance	Escape	Love	Religion
Career	Failure	Lust	Resentment
Catastrophe	Fame	Money	Resolution
Codependence	Fear	Morality	Revenge
Comfort	Friends	Outrage	Rivalry
Compassion	Frustration	Peer Pressure	Satisfaction
Contempt	Glory	Perfectionism	Self-Improvement
Contentment	Greed	Persecution	Shame
Control	Grief	Pity	Sickness
Corruption	Guilt	Pleasure	Stubbornness
Credit	Hate	Popularity	Survival
Curiosity	Honor	Power	Thrills
Cursed	Horror	Prejudice	Torment
Debt	Hurt	Prestige	Valor
Desperation	Ideology	Pride	Vengeance
Destiny	Infatuation	Protection	War
Discovery	Insanity	PTSD	Wrath

Other:

Character Archetypes

Your protagonist and antagonist are usually an amalgam of many character archetypes. The supporting characters tend to function in one of these capacities: the sidekick, love interest, mentor, fool, or nemesis.

If you want your characters to have depth, it is often good to start with an archetype, and then add other characteristics to that character.

Sample Character Archetypes		
Academic	Flatterer (Sycophant)	Politician
Anti-Hero	Foil	Priest
Athlete	Fool	Rebel
Bad Boy	Genius	Red Shirt (Cannon Fodder)
Battle-Axe	Guardian	Ruler
Black Knight	Hero	Scapegoat (Fall Guy)
Caregiver	Innocent Youth (Ingénue)	Seer
Christ-Figure	Jester	Shrew
Courtesan	Loner	Sidekick
Creator	Love Interest	Spoiled Child
Crone	Magician	Temptress
Damsel in Distress	Malcontent	Tomboy
Destroyer	Mentor	Trickster
Dirty Old Man	Miser (Scrooge)	Unwilling Hero
Doppelgänger	Mother-Figure	Villain
Explorer	Nemesis	Warrior
Everyman (Commoner)	Old Man	White Knight
Father-Figure	Orphan	Wise Elder
Femme Fatale	Outlaw	Young Lover
Other Archetypes:		

Character Traits

All characters, even good ones, should have some reasonable flaws. And in turn, characters that are purely evil often appear fake. It is best to have a healthy mix of believable traits. Here is a list to get you thinking:

Positive Traits				
Adaptable	Accepting	Adventurous	Affectionate	Amiable
Alert	Astute	Benevolent	Brave	Charismatic
Creative	Decisive	Dependable	Diplomatic	Disciplined
Earnest	Efficient	Empathetic	Enthusiastic	Ethical
Fair	Forgiving	Good-Hearted	Gracious	Happy
Hard-Working	Independent	Insightful	Intelligent	Just
Leader	Loving	Nurturing	Orderly	Patient
Passionate	Persuasive	Playful	Responsible	Resourceful
Self-Aware	Spunky	Strong	Studious	Supportive
Tactful	Tenacious	Unselfish	Watchful	Wise

Negative Traits				
Abusive	Addictive	Aggressive	Antisocial	Apathetic
Argumentative	Belligerent	Callous	Cantankerous	Childish
Clingy	Closed-Minded	Cocky	Compulsive	Cowardly
Cruel	Cynical	Dangerous	Deceitful	Defensive
Degrading	Destructive	Disloyal	Egocentric	Evil
Fearful	Fixated	Flaky	Foolish	Forgetful
Hostile	Hung-Up	Insecure	Loner	Megalomaniacal
Neurotic	Phobic	Perfectionistic	Pessimistic	Prejudiced
Manipulative	Selfish	Self-Destructive	Stubborn	Sulker
Touchy	Unreceptive	Vengeful	Whiney	Withdrawn

CRIME & DETECTIVE VOCABULARY

Are the police involved in your story? Is there a detective unraveling criminal events?

Abduction, Abuse, Access, Accident, Accuse, Action, Admission, Adult, Agency, Aggravated assault, Agree, Alarm, Alert, Alias, Alibi, Allege, APB, Appeal, Appearance, Appraise, Archives, Armed, Arraignment, Arrest, Arson, Ask, Aspect, Assailant, Assault, Assignment, Assistance, Assumptions, Atrocious, Attitude, Attack, Authenticate, Authority, Authorize, Autopsy

Backup, Badge, Badgered, Ballistics, Banned, Basis, Battery, Beaten, Behavior, Belief, Bitter, Blackmail, Blame, Bloodstain, Bodyguard, Bomb squad, Bond, Booking, Branch, Breach, Bribes, Brutal, Brutality, Bullied, Bungled, Burden, Bureau, Burglary, Busted, By-the-book

Capable, Captain, Capture, Careful, Catch, Cautious, Cease, Challenges, Character, Chase, Check out, Citation, Citizen, Civil, Claim, Code, Cold case, Colleague, Collude, Collusion, Commission, Commit, Communication, Community, Competitive, Complaints, Complicated, Concerned, Conduct, Confer, Confess, Confession, Confidential, Confrontation, Consent, Consider, Conspiracy, Conspire, Consult, Contempt, Convict, Conviction, Cooperate, Cop, Coroner, Corrupt, Counterfeit, Court, Crimes, Criminal, Crook, Cruise, Cruel, Culpable

Damage, Danger, Dangerous, Deal, Dealings, Decisions, Dedication, Deduction, Deed, Defense, Deliberate, Delinquent, Deliver, Denial, Deny, Department, Deputy, Detain, Detect, Detective, Determination, Deviant, Dialogue, Difficult, Direct, Disappearance, Discovery, Disobedient, Disorderly, Dispatch, Disregard, Distressing, Disturbing, District attorney, Documentation, Documents, Domestic disputes, Doubtful, Drugs, Drunk, Dupe, Duty, Dying

Eager, Educate, Education, Effect, Embezzle, Emergency, Emphasis, Enable, Encounter, Encumber, Enforce, Entail, Entrap, Equality, Equipment, Espionage, Ethical, Evidence, Examine, Execute, Experience, Expert, Expose, Extort, Extradition, Extreme, Eyes, Expert

Fabricated, Facts, Failure, Fairness, Family, False, Fanatic, Fault, FBI, Federal, Feisty, Felony, Fight, File, Fine, Fingerprint, Fleeting, Flight, Follow, Follow-up, Footprints, Force, Forgery, Formal charges, Foul play, Framed, Fraud, Frantic, Freedom, Full-scale, Fundamental

Gang, Ghastly, Gore, Government, Grief, Guarantee, Guard, Guilty, Gumshoe, Gun

Handcuff, Handle, Harmful, Harass, Hateful, Hazard, Heinous, Helpful, High-powered, Hijack, Hire, Hit man, Holding, Homicide, Honest, Honor, Hooligan, Horrible, Hostage, Hostile

Ill-gotten, Illegal, Illegitimate, Immoral, Imprison, Inappropriate, Incompetent, Imposed, Incapable, Indict, Influence, Informant, Information, Infringe, Initiative, Injury, Innocent, Innuendo, Inquest, Inquire, Instinct, Intelligence, Interests, Interfere, Internet, Interpol, Interpretation, Interstate, Intrude, Intuition, Invade, Investigate, Investigation, Irregular, Issue

Jaded, Jail, Jealous, Joint, Jane Doe, John Doe, Jolt, Judge, Judgment, Judicial, Jury, Justice, Juvenile

Kept out, Kidnapping, Kill, Killer, Kin, Knowledge

Laboratory, Larceny, Law, Lawful, Lawless, Lawsuit, Lease, Legacy, Legal, Legitimate, Liable, Libel, Liberty, Licensed, Lie, Lieutenant, Limit, Line up, Links, Long hours, Lurk

Mace, Magistrate, Maintain, Majority, Malevolence, Malice, Malicious, Manacled, Manner, Manslaughter, Mayhem, Menace, Minority, Miscreant, Misdemeanor, Missing person, Mission, Mob, Motivation, Motive, Motor pool, Motorist, Murder, Mystery

National, Negligence, Negotiate, Neighborhood, Notation, Notification, Nuisance

Oath, Obey, Obligation, Obscure, Obsession, Odd, Offender, Offense, Officer, Official, Omission, On-going, Open case, Opinion, Opportunity, Order, Organize, Ownership

Paperwork, Parole, Partner, Partnership, Patrol, Patterns, Payback, Pedestrian, Penalize, Penalty, Penitentiary, Penny-ante, Peril, Perjury, Perpetrator, Phony, Plain-clothes officer, Plead, Police, Police academy, Power, Precedent, Prevention, Previous, Principle, Priors, Prison, Private, Probable cause, Probation officer, Procedure, Process, Professional, Profile, Proof, Property, Prosecutor, Protection, Prove, Provision, Public, Punishment

Qualification, Quality, Quantify, Quantity, Quarrel, Quell, Query, Question, Quick, Quirks

Radar, Rank, Reading rights, Reasons, Record, Recruit, Red-handed, Redemption, Redress, Reduction, Refute, Register, Registration, Regulation, Reinforcements, Reject, Release, Report, Reports, Reprobate, Reputation, Research, Resist, Response, Responsibility, Restraining order, Restrict, Retainer, Revenge, Rights, Riot, Robbery, Rogue, Routine, Rules

Sabotage, Safeguard, Safety, Sanction, Scandal, Scene, Scum bag, Sealed record, Search and rescue team, Searching, Secret, Seize, Select, Sentence, Sergeant, Seriousness, Serve, Services, Sheriff, Shift, Shooting, Shyster, Sighting, Situation, Skilled, Slander, Slaying, Sleazy, Sleuthing, Smuggling, Snitch, Solution, Solve, Sources, Squad, Stalk, State, Statute, Statute of limitation, Stipulation, Strangulation, Study, Subdue, Subpoena, Successful, Sully, Summons, Suppression, Surveillance, Suspect, Suspected, Suspicion, Suspicious, Sworn, System

Tactics, Tantamount, Taping, Task force, Taser, Technique, Tense, Tension, Testify, Testimony, Theory, Threat, Threatening, Thwart, Tip, Torture, Trace, Traffic, Tragedy, Transfer, Trap, Trauma, Traumatize, Treatment, Trespass, Trial, Trooper, Trust, Truth

Unacceptable, Unauthorized, Unclaimed, Unconstitutional, Undercover, Underpaid, Unintentional, Unit, Unjust, Unknown, Unlawful, Uphold, Urgency, Utilize

Vagrant, Vandalism, Vanish, Venomous, Verdict, Verification, Victim, Victimize, Vicious, Viewpoint, Vigilante, Villain, Violate, Violation, Violence, Volume, Vow

Wanted, Wanton, Ward, Warped, Warrant, Watch, Weapon, Weird, Whodunit, Wicked, Wild, Will, Wiretap, Wisdom, Witness, Worried, Wrong, Wrongdoing

Yappy, Yell, Yonder, Young, Youth	Zap, Zeal, Zealous, Zest, Zero, Zilch, Zippy

Words for Sounds

Add appeal to your writing by making a splash with descriptive sound words.

Ahem	Clatter	Grind	Pound	Splash	Tweet
Baa	Click	Groan	Pow	Splat	Vroom
Babble	Clink	Gulp	Pulsing	Splinter	Wail
Bang	Clomp	Gurgle	Purr	Sputter	Wallop
Bark	Clonk	Guzzle	Quack	Squawk	Whack
Beat	Clop	Hammer	Racket	Squeak	Wheeze
Beep	Cluck	Hiss	Rap	Squish	Whicker
Bellow	Clunk	Hoot	Ratchet	Stomp	Whinny
Blare	Crackle	Howl	Rattle	Suck	Whip
Blast	Crash	Hubbub	Revved	Swish	Whir
Blip	Creak	Hum	Ring	Swoop	Whisper
Blop	Crinkle	Jangle	Rip	Swoosh	Whistle
Blow	Crunch	Jingle	Roar	Tap	Whiz
Boing	Din	Kerplunk	Rumble	Tatter	Woof
Bong	Ding	Knock	Rushing	Tee-Hee	Woot
Boo	Discord	Lash	Rustle	Throb	Yap
Boom	Drip	Mew	Scream	Thud	Yawp
Bop	Drone	Mewl	Screech	Thump	Yelp
Bray	Drum	Murmur	Scuff	Thunder	Yip
Bubble	Eek	Neigh	Shriek	Thwack	Yowl
Burp	Fanfare	Oink	Shuffle	Tick	Zap
Buzz	Fizz	Ooze	Sizzle	Tinkle	Zip
Cacophony	Fizzle	Patter	Slam	Titter	Zoom
Cha-Ching	Flick	Peal	Slap	Tock	
Cheep	Fling	Peep	Slop	Tolling	Other:
Chime	Flop	Pew	Slurp	Toot	
Chirp	Fracas	Pitter-Patter	Smack	Trill	
Chug	Giggle	Plink	Snap	Tromp	
Clack	Glug	Plod	Snicker	Trumpet	
Clamor	Glurp	Plop	Snigger	Tsk	
Clang	Gnashing	Plunk	Snip	Tumult	
Clank	Gobble	Poof	Snort	Tut	
Clap	Grating	Pop	Spatter	Twang	

Character Emotions & Moods

Above-board, Accepting, Accommodating, Acknowledgment, Active, Altruism, Ambitious, Amiable, Amicable, Appreciation, Articulate, Aspiration, Assertive, Asset, Attentive, Attitude
Benevolent, Bond, Brave
Caring, Character, Charisma, Charity, Charm, Cheerful, Civility, Clean, Coherent, Comfortable, Commitment, Common-sense, Communicative, Community, Compassion, Compliments, Compromising, Concern, Confidence, Conscientious, Conservative, Consideration, Constant, Content, Control, Cooperation, Cooperative, Cordiality, Courage, Courageous, Courteous, Creative, Creativity, Curiosity
Decent, Deferential, Dependable, Desire, Determination, Devoted, Dignity, Diligent, Diplomatic, Directed, Discipline, Discreet, Docile, Donor, Dynamic, Dynamism
Earnest, Empathetic, Encouragement, Endurance, Energetic, Enthusiastic, Equality, Esteemed, Estimable, Ethical, Euphoric, Evaluate, Excellence, Expectant, Experience, Extrovert
Fairness, Faith, Faithful, Feeling, Flexible, Focus, Forgiving, Forte, Fortitude, Friendship
Generosity, Genial, Genteel, Gentle, Genuine, Gift, Goodness, Grace, Gracious, Gratitude, Guidance
Happy, Harmonious, Healing, Helpfulness, Honesty, Honor, Honorable, Hopeful, Humble, Humility
Idealistic, Imaginative, Impartiality, Industrious, Ingenuous, Innocence, Innocent, Innovative, Insightful, Inspirational, Instructive, Integrity, Introvert, Intuitive, Inventive, Investigative
Jocular, Jocund, Jolly, Jovial, Joyful, Jubilant, Judgment, Just
Kind, Kindness, Kindred, Kinship
Laughter, Leadership, Legitimacy, Lenient, Liberal, Listener, Loving, Loyalty
Manners, Mastery, Merciful, Meritorious, Meticulous, Missionary, Moderate, Modesty, Motivation
Naive, Neatness, Needy, Negative, Nice, Noble
Obedience, Observant, Open, Open-minded, Opportunist, Optimism, Orderly, Oriented, Outspoken
Patience, Patient, Patriot, Peaceful, Peacemaker, Perceptive, Perseverance, Persistence, Personable, Personal, Philanthropic, Placid, Poise, Polite, Popular, Potential, Powerful, Praise, Pressure, Principled, Priorities, Prolific, Promptness, Proper, Punctual, Purposeful
Quality, Quick, Quiescent, Quintessential
Rational, Reasonable, Recognition, Refined, Reflective, Regard, Reliance, Remorseful, Resilience, Resolute, Resourceful, Respect, Responsibility, Responsible, Responsive, Restraint, Reverent, Righteous
Sagacious, Sage, Samaritan, Self-control, Self-esteem, Selflessness, Sensible, Sensitive, Sharing, Sincerity, Skill, Sober, Solemn, Solitary, Special, Speculation, Sportsmanship, Staunchness, Steadfast, Success, Successful, Supportive, Sweet, Sympathetic
Tactful, Talent, Teamwork, Temperament, Temperate, Tenacious, Tendency, Tender, Thankful, Thoughtfulness, Thrifty, Tolerance, Tolerant, Tone, Trait, Tranquil, Trustworthy, Truthful
Ultimate, Understanding, Unique, United, Unity, Upright, Upstanding
Values, Veracious, Veracity, Versatile, Vigilant, Vigorous, Virtuous, Visible, Vision, Vivacious, Vocal
Warm, Watchful, Welcoming, Wild, Willingness, Winning, Winsome, Wisdom, Wise, Worker, Worrier

Yearning, Yielding, Yourself	Zeal, Zealous, Zest

Tastes and Aromas

When you are writing, try to incorporate all four of the senses in your work. Here is a cheat sheet for tastes and smells:

POSITIVE	NEUTRAL	NEGATIVE	SPICES	Most Fragrant Florals
Aromatic	Acidic	Biting	Cajun	Angel's Trumpet
Citrusy	Acrid	Bitter	Cinnamon	Flowering Plum
Comforting	Airy	Decay	Clove	Heliotrope
Crisp	Ancient	Dirty	Coriander	Honeysuckle
Delicate	Brackish	Fetid	Cumin	Jasmine
Delicious	Burnt	Foul	Dill	Lavender
Exquisite	Delicate	Funky	Pepper	Lilac
Fragrant	Feminine	Gamy	Sage	Mexican Orange
Fresh	Fermented	Harsh	Thyme	Mock Orange
Fruity	Masculine	Moldy	Basil	Rose
Full-bodied	Floral	Musty	Barbeque	Star Magnolia
Hard	Humid	Nasty	Bay Leaf	Sweet Peas
Heady	Light	Noxious	Curry	Tuberose
Juicy	Medicinal	Old	Anise	
Lemony	Medium	Pungent	Caraway Seed	**Household Smells**
Rich	Mellow	Putrid	Cardamom	Babies
Savory	Metallic	Rancid	Cayenne	"Boy" Smell
Sharp	Mild	Rank	Cumin	Bacon
Succulent	Minty	Repulsive	Dill	BBQ
Sugary	Moist	Rotting	Fennel	Beer
Sweet	Musky	Skunky	Garlic	Books
Tangy	Nippy	Sour	Ginger	Bread
Tart	Nutty	Spoiled	Mace	Burning Wood
Tempting	Peppery	Stagnant	Marjoram	Chocolate
Warm	Perfumed	Stale	Mint	Cinnamon
Woody	Salty	Stench	Mustard	Citrus
Zesty	Woodsy	Stinking	Onion	Coconut
Zingy	Yeasty	Stuffy	Orange Peel	Coffee
			Lemon Peel	Cut Grass
Other:	Other:	Other:	Nutmeg	Dirty Laundry
			Rosemary	Fresh-baked Cookies
			Saffron	Fresh Laundry
			Turmeric	Pine
			Vanilla	Soap

Synonyms

As you are editing, it is important to pay attention to repetition. Much of the tinkering with words will come with editing, but I love using synonym sheets to cut down on the editing later, as well as to inspire me.

Emotions

Other words for Happy

Alluring, amused, appealing, appeased, blissful, blithe, carefree, charmed, cheeky, chipper, chirpy, content, convivial, delighted, elated, electrified, ecstatic, enchanted, enthusiastic, exultant, excited, fantastic, fulfilled, glad, gleeful, glowing, gratified, idyllic, intoxicating, jolly, joyful, joyous, jovial, jubilant, light, lively, merry, mirthful, overjoyed, pleased, pleasant, radiant, sparkling, savoured, satisfied, serene, sunny, thrilled, tickled, up, upbeat, winsome, wonderful.

Other words for SAD

Aching, agitated, anguished, anxious, bleak, bothered, brooding, bugged, chagrined, cheerless, darkly, disillusioned, disappointed, disenchanted, disheartened, dismayed, distraught, dissatisfied, despondent, doleful, failed, faint, frustrated, glazed, gloomy, glowering, haunted, hopeless, languid, miserable, pained, perturbed, sour, suffering, sullen, thwarted, tormented, troubled, uneasy, unsettled, upset, vacant, vexed, wan, woeful, wounded.

Other words for Mad

Affronted, aggravated, agitated, angered, annoyed, bitter, boiling, bothered, brooding, bugged, bummed, cantankerous, chafed, chagrined, crabby, cross, disgruntled, distraught, disturbed, enflamed, enraged, exasperated, fiery, fuming, furious, frantic, galled, goaded, hacked, heated, hostile, hot, huffy, ill-tempered, incensed, indignant, inflamed, infuriated, irate, ireful, irritated, livid, maddened, malcontent, miffed, nettled, offended, peeved, piqued, provoked, raging, resentful, riled, scowling, sore, sour, stung, taut, tense, tight, troubled, upset, vexed, wrathful.

Other words for Crying

Bawling, blubbering, gushing, howling, lamenting, moaning, scream-crying, silent tears, sniffling, snivelling, sobbing, sorrowing, teary, wailing, weepy, woeful.

Other words for Afraid

Alarmed, apprehensive, chicken, cowardly, craven, dismayed, faint-hearted, fearful, frightened, hangdog, horrified, horror-struck, nervous, panicked, panicky, panic-stricken, scared, terrified, unnerved, white-lipped.

Commonly Used Words

Other words for ASKED

Appealed, begged, beckoned, beseeched, besieged, bid, craved, commanded, claimed, coaxed, challenged, charged, charmed, cross-examined, demanded, drilled, entreated, enchanted, grilled, implored, imposed, interrogated, invited, invoked, inquired, insisted, needled, ordered, pleaded, petitioned, picked, probed, pried, pressed, pumped, pursued, put through the wringer, put the screws down, questioned, queried, quizzed, requested, required, requisitioned, roasted, solicited, summoned, surveyed, sweated, urged, wanted, wheedled, wooed, worried, wondered.

Other words for REPLIED

Acknowledged, answered, argued, accounted, barked, bit, be in touch, boomeranged, comeback, countered, conferred, claimed, denied, echoed, feedback, fielded the question, get back to, growled, matched, parried, reacted, reciprocated, rejoined, responded, retorted, remarked, returned, retaliated, shot back, snapped, squelched, squared, swung, vacillated.

Other words for LAUGH

Break up, burst, cackle, chortle, chuckle, crack-up, crow, giggle, grin, guffaw, hee-haw, howl, peal, quack, roar, scream, shriek, snicker, snigger, snort, split one's sides, tee-hee, titter, whoop.

Other Words for LOOK

Address, admire, attention, audit, babysit, beam, beholding, blink, bore, browse, burn, cast, check, comb, consider, contemplate, delve, detect, discover, disregard, distinguish, ensure, evil eye, examine, explore, eye, eyeball, ferret, fix, flash, forage, gander, gaze, get an eyeful, give the eye, glance, glare, glaze, glimmer, glimpse, glitter, gloat, goggle, grope, gun, have a gander, inquire, inspect, investigate, judge, keeping watch, leaf-through, leer, lock daggers on, look fixedly, look-see, marking, moon, mope, neglect, note, notice, noting, observe, ogle, once-over, peek, peep, peer, peg, peruse, poke into, scan, pout, probe, pry, quest, rake, recognize, reconnaissance, regard, regarding, renew, resemble, review, riffle, rubberneck, rummage, scan, scowl, scrutinize, search, seeing, sense, settle, shine, sift, simper, size-up, skim, slant, smile, smirk, snatch, sneer, speculate, spot, spy, squint, stare, study, sulk, supervise, surveil, survey, sweep, take stock of, take in, trace, verify, view, viewing, watch, witness, yawp, zero in.

Other words for WENT

Abscond, ambled, approached, avoided,
be off, beat it, bolted, bounced, bounded, bugged out, burst,

carved, cleared out, crawled, crept, cruised, cut and run,
danced, darted, dashed, decamped, deserted, disappeared, ducked out,

escaped, evaded, exited,
fared, fled, floated, flew the coop,

galloped, got away, got going, got lost, glided, go down, headed south,
hightailed, hit the road, hoofed it, hopped, hotfooted, hurdled, hustled,

journeyed, jumped,
leapt, left, lighted out, loped, lunged,

made a break for it, made haste, made for, made off, made tracks, marched,
moseyed, moved, muscled, neared, negotiated,

paced, paraded, passed, pedaled, proceeded, progressed, pulled out, pulled,
pushed off, pushed on,

quitted,
retired, retreated, rode, ran along, ran away, rushed,

sashayed, scampered, scooted, scrammed, scurried, scuttled, set off, set out,
shot, shouldered, shoved off, shuffled, skedaddled, skipped out, skipped, skirted,
slinked, slipped, soared, split, sprang, sprinted, stole away, steered clear, stepped
on it, strolled, strutted, scurried, swept,

took a hike, took flight, took leave, took off, threaded, toddled, tottered, trampled,
travelled, traversed, trekked, trode, trudged, tumbled,

vamoosed, vanished, vaulted, veered,
walked off, wandered, weaved, wended, whisked, withdrew, wormed,
zig-zagged, zipped, zoomed.

Other words for SAID

Accused, acknowledged, added, addressed, admitted, advised, affirmed, agreed, alleged, announced, answered, apologized, approved, argued, articulated, asked, asserted, assured, attested, avowed, barked, bet, bellowed, babbled, begged, bragged, began, bawled, bleated, blurted, boomed, broke in, bugged, boasted, bubbled, beamed, burst out, believed, brought out, confided, crowed, coughed, cried, congratulated, complained, conceded, chorused, concluded, confessed, chatted, convinced, chattered, cheered, chided, chimed in, clucked, coaxed, commanded, cautioned, continued, commented, called, croaked, chuckled, claimed, choked, chortled, corrected, communicated, claimed, contended, criticized, construed, dared, decided, disagreed, described, disclosed, drawled, denied, declared, demanded, divulged, doubted, denied, disputed, dictated, echoed, ended, exclaimed, explained, expressed, enunciated, expounded, emphasized, formulated, fretted, finished, gulped, gurgled, gasped, grumbled, groaned, guessed, gibed, giggled, greeted, growled, grunted, hinted, hissed, hollered, hypothesized, inquired, imitated, implied, insisted, interjected, interrupted, intoned, informed, interpreted, illustrated, insinuated, jeered, jested, joked, justified, lied, laughed, lisped, maintained, muttered, marveled, moaned, mimicked, mumbled, modulated, murmured, mused, mentioned, mouthed, nagged, noted, nodded, noticed, objected, observed, offered, ordered, owned up, piped, pointed out, panted, pondered, praised, prayed, puzzled, proclaimed, promised, proposed, protested, purred, pled, pleaded, put in, prevailed, parried, pressed, put forward, pronounced, pointed out, prescribed, popped off, persisted, protested, questioned, quavered, quipped, quoted, queried, rejected, reasoned, ranted, rasped, reassured, reminded, responded, recalled, returned, requested, roared, related, remarked, replied, reported, revealed, rebutted, retorted, repeated, reckoned, remembered, regarded, recited, resolved, reflected, ripped, rectified, reaffirmed, snickered, sniffed, smirked, snapped, snarled, shot, sneered, sneezed, started, stated, stormed, sobbed, stuttered, suggested, surmised, sassed, sputtered, sniffled, snorted, spoke, stammered, squeaked, scoffed, scolded, screamed, shouted, sighed, smiled, sang, shrieked, shrilled, speculated, supposed, settled, solved, shot back, swore, stressed, spilled, told, tested, trilled, taunted, teased, tempted, theorized, threatened, tore, uttered, unveiled, urged, upheld, vocalized, voiced, vindicated, volunteered, vowed, vented, verbalized, warned, wailed, went on, wept, whimpered, whined, wondered, whispered, worried, warranted, yawned, yakked.

My Synonym Lists:

Other Notes & Research

Books by Robin Woods

Fiction

Allure: A Watcher Series Prequel

The Unintended: The Watcher Series Book One

The Nexus: The Watcher Series Book Two

The Sacrifice: The Watcher Series Book Three

The Fallen: Part One: Watcher Series Book Four

The Fallen: Part Two: Watcher Series Book Five

Light & Shadow: The Watcher Series Shorts & Extras

Non-Fiction

Prompt Me Workbook & Journal

Prompt Me Again Workbook & Journal

Prompt Me More Workbook & Journal

Prompt Me Sci-Fi & Fantasy Workbook & Journal

Prompt Me Romance Workbook & Journal

Prompt Me Novel Fiction Writing Workbook & Journal

Prompt Me Horror & Thriller Workbook & Journal

Prompt Me Reading: Literary Analysis & Journal

Prompt Me Mystery & Suspense Workbook

Picture This: Photo Prompts & Inspiration (Digital Book)

Dive into a genre and empower your creativity.

Prompt Me Sci-Fi & Fantasy

All new photos and prompts

New activities

More master lists

More inspiration

Prompt Me Romance

Picture This: Photo Prompts & Inspiration

Meet *Prompt Me's* Digital Cousin
52 Full Color Photo Prompts
92 Written Prompts with 422 combinations
14 Master Lists
Tip, Tricks, and Challenges

Great for writers on the go!

About the Author

Robin Woods is a former high school and university instructor with two and a half decades of experience teaching English, literature, and writing. She has earned a BA in English and an MA in education.

In addition to teaching, Robin Woods has published six highly-rated novels and has multiple projects in the works.

When Ms. Woods isn't teaching or writing, she is chasing her two kids around and spending time with her ever-patient husband.

For more information and free resources, go to her website at:

www.RobinWoodsFiction.com

If you enjoyed this workbook, I would be very grateful for a review. Thank you!

Make your own die.

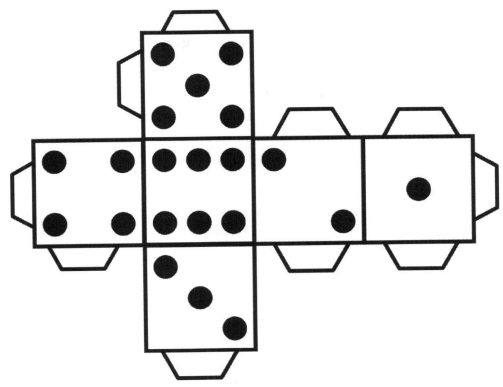

Caesar Cipher. Add intrigue by sending secret messages.

Made in the USA
Monee, IL
18 November 2023

46877870R00094